The Mind bender Book

100 favorites from the most popular radio contest in the world!

VOLUME 1

Dom Testa

ILLUSTRATIONS BY
Shannon Parish

Profound Impact Group, Inc.

The Mindbender Book
Volume 1

First Edition

Copyright © 2012 by Dom Testa

Illustrations by Shannon Parish
Interior and cover design by Rebecca Finkel, F&P Graphic Design

Library of Congress Control Number: 2011933432

ISBN: 978-0-9760564-6-1

Printed in Canada

The Mindbender: A Brief History

In late January of 1993 I was brought aboard a radio station called (at the time) Magic 100, a middle-of-the-pack station in Denver that was trying very hard to be inoffensive in any way. It was your typical in-office, background-music station, which unfortunately played too much Celine Dion, and had been through multiple name and slogan changes over the years. Although the staff was very good, the station seemed to lack any punch. My job, as the new morning show host, was to inject a sense of fun, and one of the first ways I did that was to incorporate the listeners into the show. Fun discussion topics encouraged listener phone calls, unique and interesting contests replaced the typical "be caller number ten" style, and we stopped playing so much Celine.

But without a doubt, the biggest injection of fun came from a simple feature during the seven o'clock hour each morning. And now, eighteen years later (as of this writing), and with the radio station now known as Mix 100, The Mindbender has become an institution in Denver radio. Contrary to what outsiders think, it's not a trivia contest. Trivia involves questions like, "What's the capital of North Dakota?" or "What was the first number one record that used a cowbell?" In other words, you either know it or you don't. For the Mindbender, I searched for questions that allowed everyone to play, because even if you didn't know the answer, you could perhaps puzzle it out.

Two weeks after starting at Magic 100, I discovered how fun it could be for people when I tossed out this Mindbender on February 4, 1993:

"On an average day, this form of transportation carries more people in the world than any other."

The phones went crazy. Is it cars? No. What about bicycles? No. Well, how about boats? No.

And on it went. I discovered that people were laughing as they played, because it shouldn't be that hard, right? And when, twenty minutes later, I gave enough clues to practically give it away, one person was triumphant: Elevators!

The legacy of the Mindbender was born. In the almost two decades since, there have been some classics, and some that just make people groan. Along the way I noticed something important about this fun little feature: It was bringing families together. I'm not trying to be corny here, but the comment I most often hear from listeners is, "We never miss the Mindbender as we take our kids to school." Or: "If my kids don't hear the Mindbender answer before they get out of the car, it's the first thing they want to know when I pick them up." Or: "Our family uses the Mindbender at dinner every night."

It also has become a staple in many offices. I hear stories of the Mindbender posted in workplace kitchens, or inserted into company newsletters. More than one multinational business uses the Mindbender with their associates across the ocean. How cool is that?

I appreciate the overwhelming support that my radio listeners have given this feature for so long, and to each of you I dedicate this first volume. And, more importantly, by purchasing it you're helping the state of education. A portion of the proceeds from every Mindbender book will be invested in my non-profit education foundation, The Big Brain Club. You'll find additional information about this foundation on the following pages. Please take the time to check out its web site, and to make an additional donation if it moves you.

In eighteen years, I've produced more than 4,000 Mindbenders. I hope you enjoy the 100 that you find in this first volume, lifted at random from the reams of records that I've kept since that first day. And stay tuned, because Volume 2 will be out soon!

You can listen online to the Mindbender each weekday morning at around 7:30AM (Mountain time zone) by logging on to Mix100.com.

Thank you very much for your support, by listening to the Dom and Jane Show on Mix 100 in Denver, for making the Mindbender the most popular radio contest in the world, and for purchasing the book. *Have fun!*

How This Book is Organized

Most people enjoy a little healthy competition. I've found with the Mindbender that my radio partners seem to like the spirit of competition, too. Each day they offer their own answers, and at the end of the year we crown an annual champion (Jane and Jeremy are very competitive!).

I hear that many of our listeners do the same thing, either with family or friends, carpool groups or co-workers. One listener told me, "In our house, if you get the Mindbender right you don't have to do any of the dishes that night." Excellent! So, in that spirit of competition, I've set this book up to allow you to do the same.

Each Mindbender is followed by five blank spaces. If you're by yourself, just scribble down your answer. But if you want to compete with others, there's room for five of you to record your guesses.

No cheating! Yes, the answers are in the back, but don't venture back there until you have attempted all 100 Mindbenders. If you only do a few at a time, you might (accidentally, wink wink) see the answers to some of the others. That's not in the spirit of the Mindbender, and besides: where's the fun in cheating?

And PS: I've thrown in five bonus Mindbenders in the back of the book to get you ready for Volume 2!

If you're ready to go, turn the page!

1

When you hear this sound around the house, it's usually in the key of F, middle octave.

_____

_____

_____

_____

_____

2

Experts claim that one out
of every 250 babies born is
technically what?

_____

_____

_____

_____

_____

3

You can find seventeen different species of animals here.

_____

_____

_____

_____

_____

answers

4

There has only been one confirmed human death in history caused by one of these.

answers

_____

_____

_____

_____

_____

5

By the time I finish this sentence, this will have happened about 500 times on Earth.

_____

_____

_____

_____

_____

6

Experts tell us that this will never happen to one out of every twelve people.

7

7% of people have admitted to stealing this.

_____

_____

_____

_____

_____

8

At last count, there were 1013 buildings in the United States with signs posted that said...

_____

_____

_____

_____

_____

9

45% of Americans don't know
this about our solar system.

_____

_____

_____

_____

_____

answers

10

Only one in six married men knows this.

answers

11

37% of engaged couples said they would love to do this at their wedding, but felt that it would be unacceptable.

12

A survey of stay-at-home
moms found this to be their
#1 dream job.

_____

_____

_____

_____

_____

answers

13

You will go through approximately 121 pints of this in your life.

14

10% of couples say this tool is extremely important when it comes to communicating with each other.

_____

_____

_____

_____

_____

15

Experts say this is the most often misspelled word on grocery lists.

_____

_____

_____

_____

_____

answers

16

20% of 8-14-year-olds have one, and their parents don't know about it.

17

23% of us do this once a week,
34% of us do it twice a month,
25% of us do it once a month,
and 8% never do it...

_____

_____

_____

_____

_____

18

This is the #1 lie that men tell women.

_____

_____

_____

_____

_____

answers

19

This will probably happen 280
times this week at your house.

answers

20

When asked, "What makes you happy?" 51% of women said...

_____

_____

_____

_____

_____

answers

21

2% of American women do this
every single week.

_____

_____

_____

_____

_____

22

74% of the time these are not used and just go to waste.

_____

_____

_____

_____

_____

23

78% of us sing in the car;

48% of us sing in the shower;

13% of us sing here...

_____

_____

_____

_____

_____

answers

24

17% of people said that when they goof off at work, this is usually what they're doing.

_____

_____

_____

_____

_____

answers

25

According to some experts,
it's easier to lose weight if this
is brown.

_____

_____

_____

_____

_____

26

Experts claim that people who do this for 15 minutes a day have less stress, increase their resistance to pain, strengthen their mental capacity, and are healthier.

_____

_____

_____

_____

_____

answers

27

6% of men and 3% of women have done this on a first date.

_____

_____

_____

_____

_____

answers

28

Experts say that this should have two and a half inches of water in it.

_____

_____

_____

_____

_____

answers

29

35% of women said this was the best part about pregnancy.

answers

_____

_____

_____

_____

_____

30

2% of babies born in America
don't have one of these.

_____

_____

_____

_____

_____

31

55% of people who own this are not sure how to operate it.

_____

_____

_____

_____

_____

answers

32

The average woman will do
this 5600 times in her life.

_____

_____

_____

_____

_____

33

Only 13% of people can do this.

_____

_____

_____

_____

_____

answers

34

The typical American household keeps one of these for 17 years.

35

96% of these are purchased
by women.

answers

_____

_____

_____

_____

_____

36

If you're having a hard time communicating with someone, many experts now recommend that you try it again in this location.

_____

_____

_____

_____

_____

answers

37

One in every 1506 people have
this in common.

38

A typical American spends 1 hour,
47 minutes each day doing this.

_____

_____

_____

_____

_____

39

If you left Denver, you'd travel
about 3960 miles to get here, and
you'd be the first person to ever
see it.

answers

_____

_____

_____

_____

_____

40

These move at about 7 mph.

_____

_____

_____

_____

_____

answers

41

One-third of Americans do
this every day, and they do it
an average of 3 times a day.

_____

_____

_____

_____

_____

answers

42

The average American home
has six pounds of these.

answers

_____

_____

_____

_____

_____

43

10% of us have one of these
somewhere in our car.

_____

_____

_____

_____

_____

answers

44

Research shows that this happens after a wedding 39% of the time.

45

People who enjoy this kind of party spend an average of almost $600 per year on food and beverages for them.

_____

_____

_____

_____

_____

answers

46

A recent poll of adults found this to cause more stress than anything else.

answers

_____

_____

_____

_____

_____

47

The average American woman
has nine pairs of shoes with this
in common.

_____

_____

_____

_____

_____

answers

48

There's usually an average of 188 people here.

_____

_____

_____

_____

_____

49

15% of people say this was the first thing they can remember that scared them.

_____

_____

_____

_____

_____

50

22% of Americans do this every morning, and it's sure to drive someone else crazy.

_____

_____

_____

_____

_____

51

During your morning commute, you're most likely to do this if you're an Aries, and least likely to do it if you're a Capricorn.

_____

_____

_____

_____

_____

52

43% of Americans have had one of these on their head at least once in their life.

_____

_____

_____

_____

_____

answers

53

On average, this lasts about
46 seconds.

_____

_____

_____

_____

_____

answers

54

46% of us will do this at work one time, and then never do it again.

_____

_____

_____

_____

_____

answers

55

7% of people say they never do this at home, but they'll do it when they stay at a hotel.

_____

_____

_____

_____

_____

answers

56

You can't really tell by looking
at it, but the average one is
44 inches long.

_____

_____

_____

_____

_____

answers

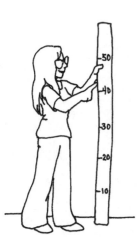

57

Surveys show that most men like these round, while most women like them straight.

_____

_____

_____

_____

_____

answers

58

When asked what kind of animal
they would like to be, 30% of
people said this.

_____

_____

_____

_____

_____

59

A survey of parents found this to be their #1 source of aggravation with their kids.

_____

_____

_____

_____

_____

60

If you have one of these in your house, there's an 85% chance you never really use it.

_____

_____

_____

_____

_____

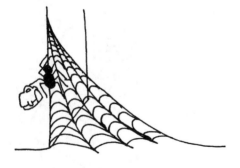

61

Unintentionally, this is where
many kids learn to read.

_____

_____

_____

_____

_____

62

47% of people said that this was their favorite thing to play with as a kid.

answers

63

When asked to name the most classic hairstyle in TV/film history, Princess Leia came in first place. Who was 2nd?

_____

_____

_____

_____

_____

64

19% of us have seen a neighbor do this.

_____

_____

_____

_____

_____

65

If you drive one mile along the average road in America, you will see eight of these.

_____

_____

_____

_____

_____

answers

66

This is the #1 thing that parents tell their kids to do.

_____

_____

_____

_____

_____

answers

67

35% of men say they will never do this without asking their wife first.

_____

_____

_____

_____

_____

68

A study of kids who performed poorly in school found that 78% of them had this in common.

_____

_____

_____

_____

_____

69

6% of people say this is why they take a vacation.

_____

_____

_____

_____

_____

answers

70

The average American will do this 9.2 times this month.

_____

_____

_____

_____

_____

71

On average, about 25 people
have handled this by the time
you buy it.

_____

_____

_____

_____

_____

72

These will, on average, only last you for about seven months, which is very frustrating.

_____

_____

_____

_____

_____

73

In a recent survey, 10% of Americans said it's impossible for them to do this.

_____

_____

_____

_____

_____

74

When adults were asked to name their most vivid memory from high school, this was the number one answer.

75

It's four feet, six inches long.

_____

_____

_____

_____

_____

4'6"

76

This is the #1 place kids hide their
Halloween candy.

_____

_____

_____

_____

_____

answers

77

This is the #1 complaint of people who go to the movies.

_____

_____

_____

_____

_____

78

It's the most common high school mascot in America.

_____

_____

_____

_____

_____

answers

79

2% of adults say they use this to treat a zit.

_____

_____

_____

_____

_____

answers

80

8% of Americans alphabetize their...

answers

_____

_____

_____

_____

_____

81

A survey asked, "What's the worst thing that could happen on your wedding day?" 53% of people said...

_____

_____

_____

_____

_____

answers

82

13% of people say they have called in sick at least once because of this.

_____

_____

_____

_____

_____

answers

83

When people were asked to name the most irritating invention of all time, this was the #1 answer.

_____

_____

_____

_____

_____

answers

84

Experts claim that 61% of
7-year-olds have one of these.

answers

_____

_____

_____

_____

_____

85

7% of people say they have found their misplaced TV remote here.

_____

_____

_____

_____

_____

answers

86

Experts say office productivity
is reduced because the average
employee spends 15-18 minutes
each day looking at this.

_____

_____

_____

_____

_____

87

21% of kids say that if they were President, they would (blank) every day.

_____

_____

_____

_____

_____

88

8% of women say a man has asked
them to do this on a first date.

_____

_____

_____

_____

_____

89

An insurance company expert has suggested that as many as 6000 car accidents each year are caused by people looking for this while driving.

_____

_____

_____

_____

_____

90

On average it lasts 5.75 seconds.

answers

91

The average person can name 285 of these.

_____

_____

_____

_____

_____

answers

92

In nature, it takes about 5 hours, 45 minutes to make an average (blank).

_____

_____

_____

_____

_____

answers

93

2% of people admit they've done this at a restaurant.

_____

_____

_____

_____

_____

94

71% of people in a relationship said they have to do this every time, because their significant other never will.

_____

_____

_____

_____

_____

answers

95

Of all the women who have one,
36% say that it's pink.

_____

_____

_____

_____

_____

answers

96

16% of mothers say that they either ate this while pregnant, or at least craved it.

_____

_____

_____

_____

_____

answers

97

A poll asked: Besides money
and food, what would you like
a lifetime supply of? This was the
top answer.

_____

_____

_____

_____

_____

answers

98

36% of married men in America have never done this.

answers

_____

_____

_____

_____

_____

99

When people were asked what sound they'd love to wake up to, "birds" was the #1 answer. This was #2.

_____

_____

_____

_____

_____

100

Men were asked to name the oldest thing they have, and this was the #1 answer.

_____

_____

_____

_____

_____

answers

answers
no peeking!

answers

1. The humming of a housefly

2. A genius

3. A box of animal crackers

4. A meteorite

5. Lightning strikes

6. Catch a cold

7. Toilet paper

8. "George Washington slept here"

9. That the sun is a star

10. His wife's weight

11. Include their pets in the ceremony

12. Best-selling novelist

13. Tears

14. A Post-It Note

15. Mayonnaise

16. A secret email account

17. Change/wash their sheets

18. "I'll never lie to you"

19. The refrigerator door opens

20. Sleep

21. Get a manicure

22. Leftovers in the fridge

23. In the elevator

24. Just looking out the window

25. Your kitchen

26. Write in a journal or diary

27. Said "I love you"

28. A bird bath

29. Choosing the baby's name

30. A middle name

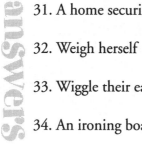

31. A home security system

32. Weigh herself

33. Wiggle their ears

34. An ironing board

35. Candles

36. In the car

37. They were born on Leap Day

38. Absolutely nothing

39. The center of the Earth

40. Raindrops

41. Hit the snooze button

42. Pennies

43. A french fry

44. The groom carries the bride over the threshold

45. Tailgate parties

46. Moving

47. She never wears them

48. A wedding

49. A ferris wheel

50. Leave a gob of toothpaste in the sink

51. Sing along to the radio

52. Mickey Mouse ears hat

53. A red light

54. Record the outgoing voicemail greeting

55. Take a bath

56. A coat hanger

57. Pretzels

58. A dolphin

59. Being a picky eater

60. A piano

61. The backs of cereal boxes

62. Swing set

63. Marge Simpson

64. Go outside in their underwear

65. Potholes

66. Close the door

67. Adjust the thermostat

68. They didn't eat breakfast

69. To get away from their pets

70. Eat at a fast food restaurant

71. A greeting card

72. Sunglasses

73. Keep a secret

74. Their locker

75. The nose on the Statue of Liberty

76. Under their bed

77. It's too loud

78. Eagles, followed by Tigers

79. A paper clip

80. Spices

81. A zit

82. They were out of coffee

83. Bagpipes

84. An imaginary friend

85. In their car

86. Their screen saver

87. Eat ice cream

88. Pay for gas

89. A french fry

90. A human yawn

91. People they personally know

92. Spider web

93. Eaten something that was ordered by someone else, but accidentally brought to them

94. Say "I'm sorry"

95. A tool kit

96. Dirt

97. Books

98. Bought flowers for their wife

99. Sizzling bacon

100. A baseball glove

Bonus Mindbenders

Here are five extra Mindbenders at no charge! There's just one slight catch: If you want the answers, you'll have to pick up *The Mindbender Book, Volume 2!* Hey, no whining!

1. 47% of us do this ourselves, 39% have someone do it for us, and 14% never do it at all.

2. There will be about 31,557,000 of these this year.

3. Your average kid in America will eat 33 quarts of this each year.

4. 79% of Americans use their lunch break from work to do this.

5. One in twelve American women describe this as the biggest nightmare in their life.

All of the answers can be found in *The Mindbender Book,* Volume 2. For information, just visit DomTesta.com. *Have fun!*

By purchasing this book, you've helped to support
The Big Brain Club

One of my deepest passions is helping young people recognize that Smart Is Cool. Sadly, millions of students intentionally dumb down because they don't want to be labeled a nerd or a dork. They desperately want to be considered one of the "cool" kids. But the day they walk out of high school they get a very cold slap of reality: suddenly, nobody cares how cool you were in school. Now all anyone cares about is what you know and what you can do.

The Big Brain Club is not about straight A's or the honor roll (although we're fans of both!). It's about helping young people to become the very best version of themselves, which begins with a solid education. Governments, parent groups, and school administrators can argue all day about how to improve education, but unless the students themselves buy into it, we're spinning our wheels.

Besides our mission to change students' perception of education, our foundation also provides cool tech supplies to schools, and we publish the creative writing of middle school students. Learn more about our programs, and see how you and/or your company can support us, by going to BigBrainClub.com.

Thank you very much!
Dom Testa